Who's There, Fuzzy Bear?

by

Sally Doherty

illustrations by

Dubravka
Kolanovic

tangerine press®

an imprint of
■ SCHOLASTIC
www.scholastic.com

Fuzzy Bear
lived in the
forest.

He was
all alone.

Or was he?

One day Fuzzy decided to go on a picnic.
First he needed to gather some food.
He did that on his own.

Or did he?

Next Fuzzy needed to
bring something to drink.
He found a jar and some tea
and made sun tea.

He only needed
enough for one.

Or did he?

Then Fuzzy Bear
needed something
to sit on.
He wove a soft
blanket out of
leaves and
moss.

It only had to be big enough for him.

Or did it?

Fuzzy Bear found a lovely spot to enjoy his picnic. He spread out his blanket, his food, and his tea when he discovered . . .

. . . three new friends to join him.
Fuzzy was happy.